PAGASAE
(where Argo was launched)

ESSALY
me of Jason)

E

DELPHI
(home of Apollo)

C

E

TO THE
BLACK SEA
AND COLCHIS

ATHENS

NEMEA

LAKE
PHALUS   MYCENAE

TIRYNS
e of Heracles)

LERNA

TO CRETE

Since some of the names in Greek mythology are hard to say, here is how the ones in this book are pronounced.

Heracles	*Herra-kleez*	Cerberus	*Ser-ber-uss*
Hercules	*Herku-leez*	Hades	*Hay-dez*
Amphitryon	*Am-fit-ree-on*	Phrixus	*Frick-suss*
Alcmene	*Alk-may-nee*	Helle	*Helly*
Zeus	*Zuse*	Nephele	*Neff-el-ee*
Hera	*Heera*	Ino	*I-no*
Olympus	*O-lim-puss*	Hellespont	*Helly-spont*
Apollo	*A-poll-o*	Colchis	*Kol-chiss*
Delphi	*Dell-fee*	Aeetes	*I-et-ez*
Eurystheus	*Yur-iss-thuse*	Jason	*Jay-son*
Nemea	*Nem-ee-ah*	Thessaly	*Thess-a-lee*
Mycenae	*My-seen-ee*	Pelias	*Pay-lee-ass*
Hydra	*Hy-dra*	Cheiron	*Ky-ron*
Lerna	*Ler-na*	Centaur	*Sen-tor*
Iolaus	*Ee-o-lay-uss*	Argus	*Ar-guss*
Artemis	*Ar-tee-miss*	Orpheus	*Or-fews*
Erymanthus	*Erry-man-thuss-*	Castor	*Cass-tor*
Augeias	*Ow-gy-uss*	Polydeuces	*Polly-du-sez*
Stymphalus	*Stimfa-luss*	Zetes	*Zay-tez*
Crete	*Kreet*	Calais	*Kalla-iss*
Minos	*My-noss*	Tiphys	*Tiff-iss*
Poseidon	*Po-sy-don*	Argonauts	*Argo-nawts*
Thrace	*Thrayss*	Aegean	*Ee-jee-an*
Diomedes	*Dy-om-ed-ez*	Amycus	*Ammy-kuss*
Amazons	*Am-az-ons*	Phineus	*Feen-ee-uss*
Hippolyte	*Hip-ollit-ee*	Harpies	*Harp-eez*
Geryon	*Gerry-on*	Ares	*Air-ez*
Orthrus	*Aw-thruss*	Medea	*Med-ee-ah*
Hesperides	*Hess-perry-dez*	Talos	*Tal-oss*
Atlas	*At-lass*	Corinth	*Korr-inth*

Andrew C C

The Labours of Heracles

Jason and the Golden Fleece

Famous Legends BOOK 2

by J. D. M. Preshous
with illustrations by Robert Ayton

Ladybird Books Ltd Loughborough 1975

THE LABOURS OF HERACLES

The most famous of all the heroes of Ancient Greece was Heracles. The Romans called him Hercules.

Heracles was born in Greece. His parents were King Amphitryon and Alcmene, but the story says that his real father was Zeus, king of the gods.

Hera, Zeus's wife, was angry and jealous because Zeus loved Alcmene, and this made her hate Heracles. When he was still only a baby, she came down from Olympus and placed two snakes beside him in his cradle. But Heracles seized a snake in each hand, and quickly crushed the terrible creatures.

As Heracles grew up, his great strength and courage became famous all over Greece. He married and his wife bore children whom he loved dearly. It seemed that Hera must have forgotten her hatred of him.

But the immortal gods who lived on Mount Olympus never forgot their love or hatred of men. Hera now struck a dreadful blow at Heracles.

One night, when he lay asleep in his palace, she drove him into a fit of madness. As in a dream he thought his enemies were attacking him. Seizing his club he lashed out until all had been killed. When the fit passed he saw the horrible truth – he had killed his own wife and children.

Not knowing that this was Hera's terrible punishment Heracles was appalled at what he had done. How could he ever escape from his guilt? He went to the temple of Apollo at Delphi and asked for help.

A voice spoke to him out of the darkness of the temple. "You will be freed from your guilt only when you have served King Eurystheus for twelve years. Do everything that he asks."

So Heracles came before King Eurystheus.
"I have come," he said, "to serve you for
twelve years. It is the wish of the gods that I
do everything you ask."

Eurystheus was a cruel and greedy king —
he hated Heracles because he was so
strong and famous. Now he seemed to have
a chance to send him to his death.

"Your first task," he said with a grim
smile, "shall be to kill the Lion of Nemea."

Only a short distance from the king's palace at Mycenae was the town of Nemea. Armed with bow and arrows and a heavy club, Heracles went to the lion's lair.

When the lion saw Heracles it leaped upon him. Heracles wounded it, but could not kill it. At last he strangled it to death. The skin made him a fine cloak, which he wore on most of his other adventures.

Heracles returned to Eurystheus, who was surprised to see him. "Very well," he said, "your next labour will be to kill the Hydra of Lerna, the dreadful water-snake."

Knowing the dangers of this task, Heracles took with him his brave young nephew, Iolaus. Together they went south to the great swamp of Lerna. Heracles knew that even the breath of the Hydra was deadly poison. In great fear they searched the swamp. Then with a terrible hissing the Hydra rose from the water.

Heracles was appalled: nine huge snake-heads swayed above its coiled body.

Drawing his sword, he struck one head off – but two more grew in its place. Then Iolaus had a plan. He made a great torch with blazing wood. Each time a head was cut off, Iolaus burnt up the neck with his torch. At last the Hydra was dead.

Then Heracles had a clever idea. Before he returned to Eurystheus, he dipped his arrows in the Hydra's poisonous blood. They might prove useful later.

The king now sent Heracles to catch the sacred deer of Artemis. This beautiful animal had horns of gold. It was very timid and Heracles had to chase it for a whole year before at last he led it back to his master.

On Mount Erymanthus in southern Greece there was a huge wild boar, which Heracles had to bring to Eurystheus. After a fierce struggle, Heracles returned to the palace, holding the wild boar alive over his head. The frightened king hid in a large jar until Heracles took the boar away.

The king angrily sent Heracles to help his friend, Augeias, who had a huge herd of cattle. He was a bad farmer and never cleaned out his stables, which were piled high with dung. Heracles was told to clean them.

The hero was very clever. He diverted the water of a nearby river so that it flowed through the stables and washed them out.

So without difficulty Heracles finished his
fifth labour. Eurystheus was angry that he
was completing his tasks so easily.

"Go to Lake Stymphalus," he said, "and
destroy the evil birds that haunt it."

Heracles, armed with his bow, set off and
found the lake. He knew that a flock of birds
lived in the reeds beside the lake – birds with
iron beaks and claws. These birds sometimes
attacked lonely travellers and tore them to
pieces.

Heracles watched, but could see no sign of them anywhere.

At last he became impatient. He made a great rattle from strips of wood and shook it in his fist. The sound echoed loudly around the mountain lake, and the birds flew screeching into the air in their hundreds.

Heracles now took his bow and shot arrow after arrow into the sky. All day he went on firing, an unending stream of arrows. The birds were all killed instantly, for the arrows were tipped with Hydra's blood.

South of Greece lay the great island of Crete. The king of Crete was Minos, who worshipped Poseidon, the sea-god. One day the god gave Minos a beautiful white bull. "Take this as a gift," he said, "but you must offer it back to me in sacrifice before long."

Minos was greedy. The bull was such a fine beast that he decided to keep it for himself. He sacrificed another white bull to Poseidon instead. But the man who thinks he can trick the gods is a fool. Poseidon was angry and drove the white bull mad. It roamed the island destroying property and killing men.

Eurystheus sent Heracles to catch the bull. Heracles stood firm as the animal charged. Using his gigantic strength, he twisted the horns of the bull until he brought it to the ground. Soon he had tamed it.

When Heracles brought the bull home alive, it was another shock for Eurystheus!

Heracles' next task took him to the other end of the Greek world – to the northern land of Thrace. Eurystheus wanted to own the wonderful mares of King Diomedes.

These horses were said to be as fast as the wind. Their master, Diomedes, was a savage king and fed the mares on the flesh of men who came to him as guests.

When Heracles came to Thrace he slew

the guards and was preparing to drive away the mares when Diomedes came up. The king rushed upon Heracles and, seizing him round the waist, tried to throw the hero to the mares. Heracles raised his club and struck Diomedes a mighty blow, stunning him.

Heracles showed no mercy to his enemies. Diomedes was thrown to the mares who devoured their own master. Then Heracles drove them back to Eurystheus.

The Greeks had many stories about a strange warlike tribe called the Amazons, who were women, ruled by a queen, Hippolyte. This queen had a gold belt, a gift from the gods. Heracles was sent to get this.

When Heracles reached the land of the Amazons he approached Hippolyte and said, "I come in peace, from King Eurystheus of Mycenae, to ask for your golden belt."

Hippolyte was pleased by Heracles'
courage, and wishing to avoid war, she
agreed to give up the belt.

This made Hera, queen of the gods, angry.
She caused a terrible battle to start. Heracles
was too strong for the Amazons. Many were
killed, including Hippolyte. Sadly Heracles
took her belt back to his greedy master.

Heracles' tenth labour was to bring back the cattle of Geryon. This giant lived in a land far to the west of Greece, and owned a herd of beautiful red cattle.

Geryon had three bodies joined at the waist, and six arms, and his watch-dog Orthrus had two heads. When Heracles started to round up the cattle, Orthrus leaped upon him, barking and snarling furiously. Heracles flung the dog from him and struck the animal a deadly blow with his club.

Hearing the noise Geryon came rushing up. Seeing the triple-bodied monster approaching, Heracles fitted an arrow to his bow and took careful aim. The arrow flew to its mark with such force that, as Geryon turned sideways to save himself, it passed through all three bodies. The giant fell dead.

Heracles drove the cattle home to Eurystheus in triumph.

Eurystheus was angry that Heracles had succeeded again, and told him to fetch the Golden Apples from the Garden of the Hesperides at the western end of the world.

The apples were guarded by a dragon. Nearby was the giant Atlas whose task was to hold up the sky. Heracles shot the dragon, then asked Atlas to reach up and pick the apples for him.

Heracles held up the sky while Atlas picked the apples. But Atlas did not want to go back to his former task. "Stay here a little longer," he said, cunningly. "I will take the apples to Eurystheus."

Heracles knew he would never return. "Very well," he said, "but the weight of the sky is very great. Take it back for a moment while I take off my lionskin and sword."

Atlas took back the sky – and Heracles picked up the apples and ran off, laughing.

When Heracles returned with the Golden Apples, Eurystheus was baffled. He could only think of one more task. "I wish to see Cerberus, the guard-dog of the Underworld," he said.

No living man was permitted to enter the Underworld, and Cerberus, the three-headed dog, was a fierce and terrible creature. Heracles, however, was quite unafraid. He descended into the dark cave that was the entrance to the Underworld, and all its guardians ran away at the sight of him.

Hades, the king of the Underworld, told Heracles that he must capture Cerberus with his bare hands. The hero had a fierce struggle with the dog, whose three heads threatened to tear him to pieces. At last Heracles dragged him up to King Eurystheus.

The king was horrified at the sight and begged Heracles to return Cerberus to Hades at once. "You are a free man," he said. "I can give you no more tasks."

So Heracles completed his Labours and went away – to find more adventures!

JASON AND THE GOLDEN FLEECE

Long ago in Greece there lived two children, a boy named Phrixus and his sister Helle. Although they were the children of a king, they were not happy. Their mother, Nephele, had gone away, and their father had married again. Their new stepmother, Ino, hated them and wanted to kill them.

One day they were walking sadly near their home when suddenly a huge ram appeared before them. It was no ordinary ram, for it had been sent by the gods to save them. Its fleece was of pure gold, and to their amazement it spoke to them.

"Climb upon my back," it said, "and I will take you away from your cruel stepmother."

They obeyed, and the ram (which could fly) carried them over the sea.

Helle lost her balance, fell and was drowned in the sea below, which was called the Hellespont, after her. Phrixus flew on safely to Colchis which was on the other side of the Black Sea, at the eastern edge of the world. Sacrificing the ram to the gods in thanks, he gave its Golden Fleece to the king of Colchis, Aeetes.

Aeetes hung it from a tree near his palace and set a great serpent to guard it.

Many years later Jason was born in northern Greece, the son of the king of Thessaly. Soon after he was born his uncle, Pelias, took away his father's kingdom and made himself king instead. He threatened to kill his nephew, so Jason was sent away.

Jason was looked after by a strange creature called Cheiron. He was a Centaur — half-man and half-horse. Jason grew into a strong young man and at last went to King Pelias to get his father's kingdom back.

Pelias had received a strange warning from the gods: "Beware of the man with one sandal!" He did not know what this meant, until one day Jason arrived.

On his way to see King Pelias, Jason had had to cross a fast-flowing river. In the middle, he had slipped, and had lost one of his sandals. When Pelias saw this, he was angry and afraid.

Jason told Pelias that he had come to claim his father's kingdom, and the king grew even more afraid. But he was cunning. "If you are to be king," he said, smiling, "you must prove your bravery."

Jason answered boldly, "I will show my bravery in any way you please."

"Then," said Pelias slowly, "you must bring me the Golden Fleece." Jason left the palace full of doubts and fears. How could he carry out this difficult task?

Then he saw what he must do. He went to Argus, the best ship-builder in the land, who built him a fine ship, with fifty oars, named the *Argo*.

Many brave men volunteered to go with Jason. There was Orpheus, the musician; Castor and Polydeuces, the twin sons of the god Zeus; Zetes and Calais, sons of the North Wind; Heracles the strong; and the steersman, Tiphys. The fifty men who sailed in the *Argo* were called the Argonauts.

When everything was ready, the *Argo* sailed out of the harbour. The Argonauts looked back as they sailed eastwards across the Aegean Sea. They saw the cloud-capped peaks of Mount Olympus. Would they ever see Greece again?

At last they came to the coast of Asia which we now call Turkey. When they landed they were met by Amycus, the king of that land. He was a gigantic, brutal man, and gave them no welcome.

"Before you leave," he roared, "one of you Greeks must fight me in a boxing match. We will see whose country produces the better men."

The challenge was accepted by Polydeuces, son of Zeus. It was a hard, cruel fight. At last, with all his strength, Polydeuces swung his fist and struck Amycus full on the side of the head. The blow was so hard that the king fell dead.

The Argonauts sailed on, and landed near a temple, where they met the blind priest, Phineus, who told them his strange story.

"Once I was a famous prophet," he said. "I had the power to see into the future. But foolishly I told men the secrets of the gods. Zeus punished me. He struck me blind and cursed me with the Harpies. Whenever I sit down to eat, these monsters swoop like lightning from the sky and devour my food. What they leave is unfit to eat."

In pity Jason offered to try to kill the
Harpies. The heroes lay in ambush while
Phineus prepared his next meal. As he sat
down to eat there was a great flapping and
screeching. The Harpies, giant birds with
human faces, appeared.

The sons of the North Wind, Zetes and
Calais, drove them away, and flew in pursuit
as far as Crete. But the gods would not let
the heroes kill the Harpies, though they did
not trouble Phineus again.

Phineus thanked the Argonauts for saving him, and told them of the dangers ahead. "At the entrance to the Black Sea are the Clashing Rocks," he said. "These rocks spring together and crush any ship that passes between them. Before you try to pass through, send a dove between the rocks. If she passes safely, so will the *Argo*."

The Argonauts left Phineus and sailed into the narrow channel. They saw ahead two towering rocks to left and to right. Jason stood on the prow of the ship and sent a dove flying ahead. As it passed between the rocks, they clashed together with a terrible grinding roar. Then they opened again, and the heroes saw that the dove had just got through.

Tiphys, the helmsman, steered the *Argo* through the gap between the rocks. As she came out, the rocks clashed again, but the heroes were safe.

So they sailed on to Colchis, and came
before King Aeetes in his palace. When they
asked for the Golden Fleece he grew angry.

"First," he said to Jason, "you must
show your courage. Go to the field of Ares,
the war-god, where you will find two fire-
breathing bulls. Harness these and plough
the field, sowing the furrows with these
dragon's teeth. Last of all you must cut the
harvest from the earth. If you do these
things, you shall have the Golden Fleece."

Jason left the palace with his friends.
They were all afraid that the trials meant
certain death. But that night Jason was
helped by an unexpected friend. Aeetes'
daughter, Medea, who was skilled in magic,
had seen him and fallen in love with him.

She met Jason secretly and gave him a
jar of magic ointment.
"No harm will come
to you if you use
this," she said.

Jason thanked Medea and made ready
for his trials. He rubbed the ointment over
his body, his armour and his weapons. It
made him feel stronger and braver as he
walked on to the field of Ares, the war-god.

The two bulls saw him coming and
charged, breathing fire. Jason seized the
first one by the horns and with a mighty
effort threw it to the ground. Then he seized
the second bull in the same way.

In their anger the bulls breathed a tornado of fire at the hero, so that he was wrapped round in flame. But the magic ointment saved him and he was unharmed.

Jason put the harness around the bulls' necks and yoked them to the plough. Then he set off up the field, cutting a deep furrow in the earth. Into the furrow he threw the dragon's teeth that Aeetes had given him.

It was evening before Jason finished sowing the dragon's teeth. Setting the bulls free again, he went back to his friends and rested. Then, taking up his weapons, he went back to the field of Ares.

He was amazed at what he saw. From the furrows were springing the tips of spears, swords and helmets. They grew into the heads and shoulders of armed men, rising from the earth. These were the Earthborn Men, the harvest that he must cut down.

Jason crouched down, hidden behind his shield. Then he hurled a large rock into the middle of the field. At once the Earthborn Men sprang at it with warlike cries and began to fight each other over it.

Jason drew his sword and hacked the men down. Some were cut down while still growing. At last the dreadful slaughter was over and Jason had finished his trials.

Night fell and Jason returned to his ship. But Medea was afraid that her father would kill the hero when he came again to ask for the Golden Fleece. So she ran away from the palace and went to the *Argo*.

She told Jason that she would help him to get the Fleece at once if he would take her away with him. So they entered the wood where the Fleece was hanging.

The serpent was awake and heard them coming. His huge head curled above Jason's head preparing to strike. Then Medea came forward casting poppy seed and magic powder into the creature's eyes. Orpheus played soft music on his lyre, and slowly the monster drooped his head in sleep.

Reaching up swiftly, Jason took the Fleece from its tree and carried it back to the ship. Before the alarm was raised, the Argonauts had set sail for Greece.

The journey home was even longer and more dangerous than before. The ships of King Aeetes cut the *Argo* off from the Clashing Rocks and so a new route had to be found. The story tells how the Argonauts sailed the length of the great river Danube and at last found their way through to the Mediterranean Sea, west of Italy.

As they came nearer home they had to pass the island of Crete.

The way was barred by Talos, the Bronze Giant. He stood on the cliffs and hurled rocks at passing ships until they sank.

When the *Argo* came near, and the frightened crew saw the huge figure raising a rock to crush them, Medea went to the front of the ship. She cursed Talos, and the bronze giant fell dead into the sea.

The Argonauts sailed on and on, and at last came home to Thessaly.

Jason at once took the Golden Fleece to Pelias. But still his uncle would not give up the throne. When Jason told Medea she used her magical powers again to help him. But this time her spells were evil, for she used them to bring a cruel death to Pelias. Telling him that she could make him young again, she set him in a huge cauldron of water. Then she boiled him alive.

The people were angry and Jason and Medea were driven out of the land. They settled in Corinth, and there Jason lived for the rest of his life. He was no longer happy, and his only joy was to sit by his dear ship *Argo*, and dream of his adventures.

As time passed *Argo* gradually began to rot away. One day, as Jason sat beneath the stern, the timbers gave way and fell upon him. This was the end of the man who made one of the very first voyages of discovery — the Quest for the Golden Fleece.

THE GODS OF ANCIENT GREECE

ZEUS was king of all the gods. He was thought to be the father of the human race and supporter of law and order. He was the god of the sky and the weather, and he regulated the seasons and the whole course of nature. His weapon was a thunderbolt or a flash of lightning.

HERA was the wife of Zeus and the most powerful goddess on Olympus. She was the goddess of marriage and women.

HADES was a brother of Zeus. His kingdom was the Underworld – the World of the Dead beneath the earth. His many-headed dog, Cerberus, guarded the entrance to the Underworld.